Chichester
GHOST TOUR

SECOND EDITION

ISBN 978-1-9164024-0-9

Compiled and edited by Julia Macfarlane.
Cover image provided by Bruce Macfarlane ©2018.

All other images supplied by
Bruce Macfarlane, Julia Macfarlane & Nick Isaac ©2017.

This book was prepared for publication by Heather Robbins.
https://hrobbinsfreelance.wordpress.com/

This guide has been produced as a collaboration between:
Bognor Regis Write Club
https://bognorwriteclub.com
and
CHINDI (Celebrating and Helping Independent authors)
www.chindi-authors.co.uk

CONTENTS

PART I

THE GHOST TOUR
Welcome

Thank you for picking up this self-guided tour to the phantoms of Chichester city centre. This is the second edition, updated in 2018, due to new stories being uncovered and some of our landmark shops closing. A guide is not much use to a stranger in town when it offers directions to the shop that used to be there.

Chichester and the surrounding villages were once the centre of smuggling, and rumours of hauntings were one of the ways smugglers used to keep nosey parkers from their stores and to explain away strange bumps in the night. So you would expect plenty of ghosts, but we suspect Chi folks are just too genteel to pass on scandalous stories of ghostly goings on. They exist but not enough for the ghoulish appetites of our writers, who were so disappointed at the dearth of ghost stories connected to such an ancient city that we decided to create some of our own to pad out the few that do exist. However, we are an honest bunch and have openly confessed each time we have strayed into fake news territory.

Enjoy your walk around our beautiful city centre and we hope our grisly imaginations don't affect your dreams too much tonight.

1. THE MARKET CROSS

We start at the Market Cross. From here, the streets of Chichester are very complicated. Pay attention. To the North is North Street; to the South is South Street; and to the East and West, you will find East Street and West Street, respectively. If you can manage this, you should be OK following our planned walk.

Let me start you off with a grisly tale from our smuggling era:

Visitors often ask why the centre of Chichester has not been fully pedestrianised. Surely it makes sense to completely close off the area around the Market Cross? Well, I wonder if it's because without the noise of traffic, you might hear other sounds. Like the creaking of a heavy cart, and the rattle of chains?

It's easy to have a romantic view of smuggling in the 8th century. Watch a few episodes of 'Poldark' and you'll know what I mean. But it wasn't just 'baccy for the Parson and lace for the Squire', as Rudyard Kipling's *A Smuggler's Song* suggests. Some of the gangs were organised and vicious, and you crossed them at your peril.

In 1748, the Hawkhurst Gang staged a raid on the Brixham customs house, and 'recovered' smuggled tea and brandy that the law had intercepted. As the Gang travelled through the New Forest with their liberated goods, they were recognised by a local man called Chater, who offered to identify them. On Valentine's Day 1748, customs officer William Galley was sent to escort Chater to Chichester to give evidence. The pair made it as far as Rowlands Castle before being ambushed by members of the Hawkhurst Gang.

Over the next two days they drunkenly tortured the two men, whipping, beating, and cutting them when they begged for mercy. The gang members' wives took no physical part but encouraged their men to do it, saying things like: "Hang them! They came here to hang you." (Hampshire women – what can I say? So different from the fragrant ladies of Chichester.) It became obvious that the gang were going to have to kill Chater and Galley but none of the smugglers had the nerve to do the job cleanly. In the end, Galley was buried alive, and Chater was thrown down a well. When the smugglers saw that he was still alive, they threw rocks at him until he stopped moving.

There was a code of silence around smuggling – people 'watched the wall as the gentlemen rode by' (to quote Rudyard Kipling again) – but this time the locals felt the smugglers had gone too far. Seven men were arrested and put on trial at the Chichester Guildhall. They were all sentenced to hang, and all but one did – Jackson, one of the ringleaders, died of heart failure whilst being measured for the gibbet chains that would display his corpse.

On the day of their execution, the men were taken the Cathedral where they listened to a sermon exhorting them to mend their ways. They didn't have long to do it, as they were then put on a cart and wheeled through the city, and an angry mob. They passed by the Market Cross, and then North to the Broyle where they were hanged. It's not a short journey. Vicious though they were, imagine how terrified the gang must have been as the cart made its way over the cobbles and through puddles – each jolt taking them closer to the scaffold.

On quieter nights, when the buses are tucked up in the depot and the cars have gone home, it is said the rattle of carts and the moans of the condemned men may still be heard at the Market Cross junction.

So perhaps we're better off with the sound of traffic …

And now to send you on your journey, turn towards West Street and make your way to the Cathedral. Look across to the opposite side of the road and admire the rooftop decorations of:

2. THE DOLPHIN & ANCHOR, 9 WEST STREET

Feel free to pop in for a swift half. There has been a hostelry of some description here since 1610 at least. It used to be the Dolphin Inn until it merged with The Anchor in 1910. What stories are concealed within its walls? Anne Caine imagined a doomed young woman committing suicide using the new-fangled 'symmeter' razor and an interesting time-slip where her ghostly presence still roams the rooms. Go to page 30 to read more.

3. CHICHESTER CATHEDRAL (PART 1)

Now turn around and gaze in awe at our city's cathedral. The death of the Bishop of Chichester is always foretold, they say, by the arrival of a heron which perches on the cathedral spire (according to *The Folklore of Sussex* by Jacqueline Simpson). If you see one perched up there today, please make sure you let a cathedral official know, so they can start preparing for the change.

4. CATHEDRAL BELL TOWER

Look across to the Cathedral and note its bell tower, a separate building at the west end. It is unusual for the bell tower to be separate from the main building but our cathedral has had a series of collapses due to subsidence. The south-west tower collapsed in 1210, the north-west tower collapsed in 1635 and was not rebuilt until 1901. The spire was built in the 14th century, repaired in the 17th century, and survived a lightning strike in 1721. However, it telescoped in on itself on 21 February 1861, fortunately without loss of life. Imagine how these sudden collapses of the cathedral might have affected the minds of superstitious people of earlier times. Thank goodness we are so much more rational these days, even people who are taking themselves on a ghost tour in the 21st century ...

5. THE DUKE & RYE, 14 WEST STREET

Time for another pub. The Duke & Rye was a 19th-century Gothic Revival church. If you like your pub with a vaulted ceiling and full of spirits (!), head inside. Like many buildings in Chichester, underneath are cellars often linking into each other through smugglers' tunnels. Sadly, although the barmaid here confirmed the spookiness of the cellars, she knew of no ghostly experiences down there.

Alongside the Duke & Rye is Tower Street, at the end of which is the Novium, Chichester's museum which spans our history from the remains of a Roman bath house to a Tim Peake exhibition. Well worth a brief deviation from the tour.

6. THE CHICHESTER INN, 38 WEST STREET

You can continue along West Street to the Chichester Inn at the end of the road, and if you are using this guide as a pub-crawl, I recommend that you do. Chichester Inn has genuine ghost stories attached to it. A Roman legionnaire has been known to brush past customers as they drink. People only ever see the top half of his body and it is believed he

must be one of the soldiers who patrolled the nearby Roman city wall. A barmaid at the Inn also reported that as she was cleaning a mirror, she saw the reflection of an old woman standing in the doorway watching. But when she turned to inform her the pub was closed – there was nobody there!

7. 51 WEST STREET

Now walk or stagger back towards the cathedral. Note the shops on your right: they used to be cottages. In one of these, or one very similar, let's say No. 51 West Street, which is now Whiteheads Estate Agents, Julia Macfarlane's grandmother had an eerie premonition during the Second World War. From the top of her stairs she saw her eldest son, from the waist up, apparently drowning and calling to her, in her hallway. As he was in the Navy, she presumed she had foreseen his death and waited with dread for the expected black-edged telegram. Read the full story on page 33 to find out what happened next

Continue down the road and just before the bell tower, head down the steps until you see:

8. THE STATUE OF SAINT RICHARD

We are sure Saint Richard was a good man in real life, but some of us find he reminds us of - dare I say it? – Nosferatu. Imagine this man leaning over you in the gloom to deliver the last rites.

9. CHICHESTER CATHEDRAL (PART 2)

Please feel free to take time to look around the Cathedral. If you can, explore the Treasury, looking out for the lead cross and plaque relating to Bishop Godfrey. There is a mystery surrounding Bishop Godfrey, who died in about 1088. The Cathedral graveyard was traditionally known as 'Paradise', but Bishop Godfrey was buried on the outskirts, almost at the point where suicides and stillbirths were buried. Not where a good bishop should have his final resting place, not tucked up inside, near the altar, as is normal for someone so exalted. And why was his ceremonial cross made of lead, rather than the usual gold, silver and gems? Lead being the material used by alchemists in medieval times to add power to magical spells or to keep something buried that has no business wandering above the earth. What did this bishop do in life that the inscription on the cross reads:

"We absolve you, O Bishop Godfrey, in place of St. Peter, prince of the Apostles, to whom the Lord gave the power of binding and releasing, so that in so far as your accusation warrants and the remission pertains to us, God the omnipotent redeemer, the kind forgiver, may be to you the healing of all your sins."

For a ghostly interpretation, read Sebastian Phillips' take on it on page 34.

page 34.

There is a legend that a faceless monk is often seen around this green, where even on the brightest days there are unusually dark corners. Keep your eyes open as you go around the cathedral and back onto West Street.

10. THE CATHEDRAL GREEN

Head back towards Market Cross, but before you reach it, take a right-hand turn and follow the path on the Cathedral green at the 'Welcome To The Cathedral' sign.

Look to your right for the gravestone of Mary Buttery, and observe the skulls thereon. No reason, they just look spooky.

Follow the path to its end and turn left through the archway to arrive outside:

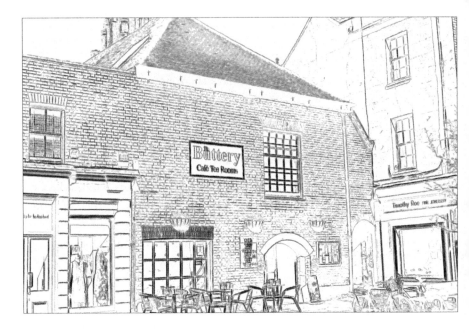

11. THE BUTTERY CAFÉ, 12A SOUTH STREET

.... which used to be the Vicar's Hall, where curates, etc. came for meals. Is it a coincidence that you have just passed Mary Buttery's grave and now you are outside the Buttery Café?

I would have said 'yes' as buttery is just an old-fashioned name for a dining place *but* the ghost that haunts this café has been nicknamed Mary by the staff. She is active enough that ghost-hunting groups have arranged visits here after closing time in the hope of experiencing her antics: pictures fall off walls and sometimes, after closing hours, when only one person is left in the building, a strange whistling is heard.

Previous research found that there was a naughty ghost reputed to haunt this café whose invisible hand pinched the waitresses' bottoms as they went about their duties. But nowadays it seems even our ghosts have turned PC and the current staff's bottoms are untouched.

This building is also the inspiration for the Keats poem of 1820, 'The Eve of St Agnes', which I am sure you all know well – right? Feel free to recite all 42 stanzas, if you can remember them. If not, here is my potted version. Basically, on St Agnes Eve (20th January), it was alleged that if a young maiden fasted all day and looked into nobody's face before she went to bed she would dream "of visions of delight and soft adorings from their loves receive". I think this can be interpreted as a promise of erotic dreams! Our heroine is young Madeline, who has already lost her true love, Porphyro, because her father banished him and had sworn that should he return her father and all his warriors would kill him. Now, as it happens, her father has a great feast planned and all his warriors have gathered together here, in the Buttery Café, where Keats imagined the great feast. Little Madeline has decided to miss out on the banquet and not to admire all the beautiful costumes swishing past her but just to go to bed. Her old nurse, Angela, knows of Madeline's plans, so imagine Angela's surprise when she finds in one of the doorways Madeline's love, Porphyro, back from his travels, and desperate to have a last look at Madeline. Angela begs him to leave, tells him he'll be killed – all his enemies are gathered here tonight – but he begs just a peek. So like all good nurses, she says, 'Oh go on then, tell you what, I'll hide you in Madeline's bedroom – but then you're off. And don't wake her up!'

'Fair enough,' the lad replies, and they sneak through the house, hide Porpyro in a cupboard and soon enough, here's Madeline sighing her hungry way to bed. And he watches her undress – oo-er missus – and go to bed. Once she's asleep, he brings out the treasures from his travels and piles them next to her bed. Then he softly plays on her "hollow lute" – I don't think this is a euphemism – and unsurprisingly, she wakes up but thinks she's still dreaming. In fact, she thinks St Agnes has surpassed her expectations. Madeline declares her love and one thing leads to another. Keats doesn't go into all the details but in the next stanza Porphyro is calling Madeline his bride so your guess is as good as mine. The deed being done, they decide they have to flee and with Angela's help out they go into the dawn.

> "*They glide like phantoms into the wide hall;*
> *like phantoms to the iron porch they glide*"

And in the last stanza:

> "*That night the Baron dreamt of many a woe,*
> *And all his warrior-guests, with shade and form*
> *Of witch, and demon, and large coffin-worm,*

Were long be-nightmar'd. Angela the old
Died palsy-twitch'd, with meagre face deform;
The Beadsman,* after thousand aves told,
For aye unsought for slept among his ashes cold."

So, a couple of random deaths at the end just to add that gothic touch. We will have more on Keats later.

12. PREZZO'S

Now look across the road to Prezzo's, which used to be The White Horse pub, reminders of which can be seen in its stained-glass windows depicting white shire horses. The manageress is haunted by a whole family of ghosts,

---

* A beadsman was a poor churchman paid to pray for the souls of others.

presumably previous owners, who still inhabit the top floor. They make themselves known when the restaurant is busy – these ghosts prefer it quiet – by calling the manageress's name and opening all the windows on their floor. One of the waiters told us it is really difficult to open these windows but the ghosts can open them all in seconds. And although these ghosts are friendly, they like to introduce themselves to new staff members by flipping piles of metal trays off shelves as they pass.

But the best story from here happened in about 2013, when the manageress herself was quite new. One of the waitresses needed accommodation for a few days and they made her up a bed on the top floor. When the manageress arrived in the morning, the poor waitress told her she had been scared out of her wits. In the middle of the night she had been awoken by someone – or something – playing with her leg, moving it up and down, and then they had scratched her chest! The marks were visible. About three months later a customer told them how he used to sleep there when the restaurant was still a pub and had had exactly the same experiences.

You could do worse than pop in now for a glass of vino or a pizza.

12. THE FOUNTAIN PUB, SOUTH STREET

Walk along South Street, resisting all the shops if you can, until you reach the Fountain Pub on your right, another pub claiming to be genuinely haunted. If you step inside, watch out for its resident ghosts: a man with a dog and a Roman soldier. You can actually see part of the Roman wall within its restaurant.

Perhaps also keep an eye out for Martians and time travellers, as in the 1820s HG Wells' grandparents ran the Fountain.

Head back towards the Market Cross and into East Street.

13. JIGSAW, 92 EAST STREET

This shop front was once the entrance to the Punch House Hotel, built in 1590 and still a bar/hotel into the 1980s. Queen Elizabeth I is said to have stayed here. But we are more interested in the body said to have been buried in the cellar walls. John Holder worked here and died in 1890, and for some reason was buried in the cellar rather than the local graveyard. When it was still a pub, staff believed his ghost was responsible for moving objects around and turning on and off the beer taps.

Current staff informed me that they still don't like the atmosphere in the basement and my report of John Holder had not helped in the least.

14. NORTH PALLANT

It is worth a walk along North Pallant, a side road just to the right of Fat Face, 83 East Street, to see Dodo House, sorry, Pallant House. No reason other than the 'dodos' are worth looking at, as is Pallant Gallery if you have time. The history of the dodos? The owner wanted ostriches, but we suspect the sculptor had never seen one and the locals duly christened the house Dodo House.

Head back towards East Street, keeping an eye out for the shades of two small children painted on the wall to your left. Why, you may ask yourself, are these two 1940s evacuees depicted loitering on a corner in Chi, and how did they make so much money?

This wall art's real name is 'The Big Deal'. To the right of these little urchins is a 'twitten' or alleyway bearing a blue plaque. Pop through to see some more street art – two giant birds nesting on the far side of the car park. More about these later.

Now, back you go to East Street, head right and look out to the left hand side for:

15. ERNEST JONES, 30 EAST STREET

Romans buried their adult dead outside the city walls but their children were buried within the city. Beneath these shops, excavations uncovered Roman children's skeletons buried in clay pots. Shop assistants working in these shops have told me that nobody likes going upstairs on their own, due to the unexplained noises and a general creepy feeling. Ironically, this shop, until recently, used to be Mothercare.

Keep going along East Street and look for the impressive Doric columns that decorate the temple to women's fashion that is currently the Next shop on your right, but used to be:

16. THE CORN EXCHANGE

This building has been a theatre and a cinema in its time. Just to show that ghosts are not only a thing from the past, Carol Thomas has linked a ghost from the Forties with a modern-day woman on page 36. Sharing a ghost's name can be more than a coincidence, it can be a call across the decades that finally catches up with you. Check your reflection in the next glass window – are you sure you're really here?

Keep going along East Street until just before the traffic lights.

17. 11 EASTGATE SQUARE & KEATS

If ever there was a photo opportunity, here it is. Have a seat next to John Keats himself. If you're hungry and can face a pie, Turner's may be selling their famous pie and mash to eat alongside Mr Keats. If you look carefully, you should also find a plaque above the Retro & Vintage shop at 11 Eastgate Square, across the road, to commemorate the fact that Keats stayed here in 1819 and began to write 'The Eve of St Agnes', inspired by the Buttery Cafe. A grisly tale from Jenny Dean relates to the Eastgate building and can be found on page 35.

Head back into East Street and keep your eyes peeled to notice the Shippams' clock and wishbone hanging above the shops on your now right-hand side, and imagine the size of the turkey that came from before it was squished into Shippams sandwich paste. Or was it one of the giant birds you saw in North Pallant car park? Now find the alley beside 21 East Street (between Halifax and Vodafone premises) signposted to the Oxmarket Gallery.

Now find the alley beside 21 East Street (between Halifax and Vodafone premises) signposted to the Oxmarket Gallery. Cross the car park, keeping to the left, and go through the archway. In front of you is:

18. ST MARY'S ALMSHOUSES, ST MARTIN'S SQUARE

There has been a building here since before the 13th century. In 1625 a local brewer built these alms houses for 12 'decayed' persons and they are still used today as shelter for the elderly.

There was a superstition in West Sussex that after a death the front door of the deceased's home must remain open until their burial, otherwise another death was sure to follow.

In the 19th century, a death occurred in these almshouses and on the morning of the funeral, once the body had left, the niece of the deceased locked the apartment door. The other almshouse residents began thumping and rattling it to force it open. And one of them exclaimed, "Hang that good-for-nothing woman! Her locking this door before the old girl is buried will bring death among us pretty soon again."

And being elderly and decayed, I expect it surely was.

With the almshouses in front of you and the public toilets to the left, follow the path until you hit St Martins Street. You should see the Stephen Laurence shop in front of you. Turn right and walk until you meet Lion Street. Head into this road.

19. COTTAGE STORY

Pick a cottage, any cottage near here, and then imagine that in a cottage very like this (or maybe one down the road in Bognor Regis) Helen Christmas had a real ghostly experience. Early one morning, the outline of an old lady shuffled past her in her own living room; there, but not there. Later, she

found an accurate description of the same old lady having lived in the house in the early 19th century. Read her account in full on page 41.

At the end of Lion Street, turn right and you will be in North Street.

20. THE OLD CROSS, 65 NORTH STREET

Time for another old pub in Chichester. Even a middle-class city like Chi had a workhouse, which used to be located on New Broyle Road, just outside the centre. Caroline Travis thinks the Old Cross might have been the favoured pub of the sour-faced master of the workhouse, Mr Dewey, who took his revenge on William Morrey, a master butcher from the Butter Market, in the most macabre way. Why not step inside and breathe in the atmosphere? Dewey took in Mr Morrey's children after the widowed butcher had drowned his sorrows in this pub. He terrified Morrey's son, Billy, to death by leaving him overnight in the Dead Room, where the paupers' corpses were kept until the undertaker could call for them. Realising he had gone too far this time, Mr Dewey needed to hide wee Billy's corpse and what better way than to throw his chopped up body into the stew pot for the workhouse inhabitants, and save money on his meat bill at the same time? Read the story in full on page 43.

Anybody fancy a meat pie? Seriously, anyone? Right next to you are Greggs and The West Cornwall Food Co., or did you indulge at Turner's when you ahd the opportunity?

Cross the road just before the end of North Street and take a look at:

21. THE CITY WALLS

Walk a little way along them. Look into the back gardens of the houses as you stand on the walls. One of these houses is now Sussex Fireplaces.

Back in the 1950s this house was a hairdressers called Avril's after Alison Jones' mother who lived here. Alison reports that:

"Many a time my Mum used to play with her imaginary friends. Being an only child, these friends were a great source of amusement. Her mother was quite a psychic person and thought nothing of it when Avril told her of the children she played with. One sticky hot summer's night the whole family were pleased that Avril had these imaginary friends for it was they that alerted her to the fact that the house was on fire. All of the family had to jump to safety from the first-floor window at the front of the house. All were saved including the family pets."

Back into North Street and head back towards the centre. Feeling thirsty? Opposite you is:

22. THE GEORGE & DRAGON, 51 NORTH STREET

This pub is another with many-roomed cellars and tunnels below it. A person could so easily get lost underneath the city, never to be found again. Becky Brooke imagined that these catacombs could also be used to get rid of troublesome commoners with dangerous secrets. Ssh – can you hear Charlie howling for help? Perhaps you should step into the George & Dragon for a pint of Dutch courage and to set the scene for Charlie's story, to be found on page 45.

Back into North Street and walk briskly to:

23. COUNCIL OFFICES & GUILD HALL

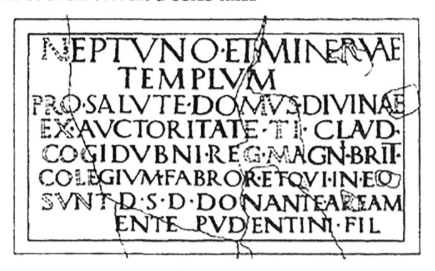

Another scene from Becky's story, the place that Charlie was heading for, before he was so cruelly intercepted. Look under the covered area for the Roman stone which mentions Cogidubnus, the tribe leader here before the Romans invaded. He seems to have become a Roman citizen rather than fighting to the death against the Roman invaders. I guess Cogidubnus would have voted 'Remain' in the Brexit referendum. Welcoming in the Europeans certainly did him no harm if this plaque is a sign of the lavishness of his gravestone, and archaeologists believe Fishbourne was probably his palace.

24. BETWEEN THE LINES, 79 NORTH STREET

This shop is the home of a ghost named Reg. At least, that is what the staff have christened him. They report a creepy feeling on the upstairs landing;

objects being knocked over or moved; and they sometimes have the feeling that someone has walked past them when there's nobody there. Most impressive of all, and proof Reg doesn't mind his nickname, is that the lights in one of the stock rooms are unreliable. Flick the switch – no lights – but the staff have learned to say: "Please, Reg, can we have the lights on?" And Reg usually obliges.

Let's walk back towards the Cross with one last stop on your left outside:

24. JONES THE BOOTMAKER, 85 NORTH STREET

This shop used to be a convivial pub, much frequented by the traders and customers from the Market Cross. Mary Jane, the bar owner's wife, was a bit of a flirt with the customers. One night her husband could bear his jealousy no more and strangled her in their bed. Full of remorse, he handed himself into the 'peelers' the next day and was duly hanged three months later. Even today, unlucky customers may feel a pair of hands tightening around their necks if the boots they are trying on are deemed too kinky for our jealous ghost. Read all about Alison Jones' version of events on page 47.

25. BACK TO THE MARKET CROSS

We hope you have enjoyed your tour. If you know of any ghost stories connected with Chichester and its buildings, please let us know by emailing bognorwriters@gmail.com and maybe the next edition of this alternative history may include your ghostly story.

PART II

THE GHOST STORIES

*For your further delectation and delight,
this section contains stories contributed by the writers of
Bognor Regis Write Club and CHINDI.*

*To be read at dusk, by candlelight and alone.
Or failing that, wherever you want, really.*

TIME SHIFT

Anne Caine

The bell-ringers were practising at the Cathedral bell tower as Bradbury checked into the Dolphin & Anchor Hotel at 7:00 p.m. exactly as planned. It was as though the bells were applauding his arrival and he felt a glow of pride as he imagined the resounding applause he would most certainly receive tomorrow. The desk clerk seemed a little flustered as he showed him to Room 13. It wasn't usually let out to guests, he explained. Bloody superstition, no doubt. Well, he wasn't one for superstition. One always found these things to have rational explanations, if one only had the aptitude for careful and logical research.

He unpacked. His suit was hung on the back of the door; his toothpaste and toothbrush stood to attention next to the sink; his lecture notes were reverently laid out on the desk; his mobile and wallet were put into the inner pocket of his overcoat ready to go out shortly. Everything in its place and everything running to time. He was ready to go out to dinner by 7.30 p.m. Just a simple supper that wouldn't take up too much time (one never took long to dine when one was spared from making small talk to a companion). He would then make his final preparations for his inaugural lecture at the University Business School tomorrow, and get an early night and a good long sleep.

The Market Cross clock struck 10:00 p.m. as he was brushing his teeth before bed. He drifted off to sleep almost straight away. He seldom had trouble sleeping, on account, he always said, of having cleared his mind and prepared thoroughly for the next day.

It was quite surprising then, and not a little vexing, that Bradbury found himself awake sometime later. He could hear a clock ticking, ticking away the wasted seconds monotonously. His senses gradually sharpened and every sinew of his body seemed to march in time to the tick-tock rhythm. Eyes blinked. Breathe in. Breathe out. Heart thumping. He lay listening, the blood pumping in his ears with each metronymic beat. Was it in fact the sound of his own heart beat? No, now it sounded more like a dripping tap. He sat up slowly, and as he hadn't drawn the curtains the street lights outside provided enough for him to see the shapes of the furniture and the doorway to the ensuite.

He staggered slowly towards the bathroom. The dripping noise was definitely louder but he couldn't find the blasted light switch to see where it was coming from. He felt his way over to the sink and reached for the taps, knocking over his toothpaste and toothbrush with a clatter like horses' hooves riding over cobbles. He tightened both taps to off. He could still hear it. He felt his way over to the bath, slipping on something wet on the floor he lurched forwards and grabbed at the shower curtain to steady himself. The wet patch on the floor was warm on his bare feet. Some idiot upstairs must have left their bath running and now it was dripping through the ceiling. A cold wind blew through the room, violently billowing the shower curtain to which he clung. Suddenly the flimsy rail fixings of the curtain gave way, and before he could grab the side of the bath to stop himself, he fell forwards and with a clang as loud as the Cathedral bells his forehead hit the edge of the toilet.

She had thought he was just late as usual and had sat in their room at the Dolphin Inn waiting for him, but as the evensong bells of the Cathedral rang she realised with a jolt what was happening. Hearing the clattering of horses' hooves down West Street, she ran to the window in time to see the stagecoach for London drawing away. She wrenched open the window and shouted out to him. But her pleas were drowned out by the bells. He was gone and she was alone. She sank down by the open window. Already feeling numb, she was unmoved by the icy wind blowing through. After some time she looked around. He had left his spare suit hanging in the open wardrobe, his new prized shaving equipment glinting on the wash stand. She walked slowly over, picking up his symmeter razor. She knew what she had to do and her resolve was as cold and hard as the steel in her hand.

Bradbury came around, his head pounding and shivering all over with cold. He began to make conscious thoughts but without any order or real comprehension. It was light now; he was lying on the bathroom floor; there seemed to be a draught … no, a breeze was blowing through the room. He lay there unaware of how much time passed. Then he heard the Market Cross clock and each chime brought him back to clearer consciousness. 10 o' clock. He was supposed to give his lecture at 10:30! How could this have happened? What *had* happened? In his panic, he sat up far too quickly causing a searing, blinding pain in his head. His vision blurred. As his eyes slowly refocused, he noticed two inexplicable things: his toothbrush and toothpaste were on the bathroom floor near a rusty coloured stain on the lino, and his lecture notes, blown by the breeze, were strewn all over the bedroom.

Could he still make the lecture? Where was his mobile phone? Should he call the University, or a taxi ... or an ambulance? He slowly rose and walked towards the bedroom. Where had he left his blasted phone? Looking around he saw that somehow the window had opened. Not that the top sash had fallen but the bottom sash was raised. What the hell had happened last night? Remembering what he was supposed to be looking for, he checked the bedside table, then gingerly bent down to peer under the bed; he looked on the desk where his lecture notes had been carefully placed; he rifled through his bag; checked the pockets of his suit hanging on the back of the door. Where was his blasted phone? So unlike him, how could he have misplaced it? He tried to remember where he had last had it. His heart pounded, making the throbbing in his forehead all the more painful. The Market Cross clock struck the half hour – 10:30. He looked down in utter bewilderment, trying to slow his breathing and grasp at an explanation. From the floor, the title page of his lecture notes stared back at him: 'Harnessing the power of time management'. He sank back to the floor, confused and defeated.

NOTES:

The story is set in 1996, the last year that the Dolphin & Anchor was still a hotel. A Grade-II Listed building, the Dolphin Inn has been in existence since 1610. It was one of only two stops in the city to board stagecoaches to London in the 18th century.

In mid-1700s products for men to shave themselves with began to be manufactured and advertised. 'Time Management' began to enter the public consciousness and to be adopted by businesses in the 1990s, when increased competition, downsizing and the increase in online working enabled improved data collection and analysis.

II

THE COTTAGE VISION

Julia Macfarlane

During the Second World War, a mother, whose eldest son was in the Navy, stood at the top of her stairs at eleven o'clock one morning, transfixed by the vision she saw below her. Seemingly knee-deep in the hall floor by her front door was her son, in his naval jacket, clear as day, calling out to her: "Mum! Mum! Help me, Mum!" The poor woman knew there and then that her son was drowning somewhere in the Atlantic. She waited in dread for the telegram boy to deliver the fateful message that her son was yet another victim of the war.

But three weeks later there was a knock at the door, and instead of the telegram boy, it was her son, home on unexpected leave. You can imagine her joy. Later that day, settled down back in his family home the young man began to tell tales of his adventures fighting the Germans. "Three weeks ago," he said to his mum and sisters, "I fell overboard early one morning, never been so scared in all my life. And you wouldn't believe it, mum, but I shouted for you, as loud as I could. As if that would have helped me!" Closer questioning and they realised that his early morning dip was at exactly the same time that his mother had seen her vision.

True story, the mother was my grandmother.

NOTES

For the sake of historical accuracy, I need to say that while this story is true, it happened in County Durham, not West Sussex.

III

WHAT THEY FOUND IN PARADISE

Sebastian Phillips

They found the stone coffin in 1860, and then four years later they found the cross which should have been on the occupant's chest. The words on it read:

> *"We absolve you, O Bishop Godfrey, in place of St. Peter, prince of the Apostles, to whom the Lord gave the power of binding and releasing. On 25th September, on the feast of St Fermin, Bishop Godfrey of Chichester died. On the same day it was five days after the new moon."*

It was the only mention of a Bishop Godfrey which local historians could find, and they left it at that. Medievalists were confused because they didn't know of a Godfrey who held the See between Stigund and Ralph de Luffa. Mind you, there was chronological space for another bishop. After Stigund's death the See was thought to have been vacant for more than ten years. So Godfrey was officially named Chichester's second bishop. A few historians scratched their heads while they sipped their port – odd thing, a prelate being wiped from the records that way – but there he was.

The antiquarians were also confused. The cross turned out to be made of lead. Why not gold or silver? It was not uncommon for a Bishop to be interred with the chalice he had used during his services. Where was that? Grave robbers perhaps. And why was he buried outside the church? 'Paradise' might be good enough for the common folk but a bishop would prefer to be tucked up by the altar. The burial was out by the very northern edge, with the suicides and stillbirths. But they were antiquarians and even more addicted to port than historians, so they forgot about it.

The folklorists also wondered. Why did a bishop need a pardon from Rome before he could be buried in consecrated ground – if you could call that end of Paradise consecrated? These were times when a bishop had to be a politician and we know how many crimes *they* commit, but a lot of time and money went into getting this distinctive wording. They were puzzled as they sipped their cider.

But the thing which puzzled them most was the cross being made of lead. Because that was used a lot in medieval magic. There are charts where it stands as the opposite of the moon. Iron was good for fey folk, but lead would give you a good curse, or lay something back into the earth. Something which had no business being out of it.

Three different academic disciplines, all with different stories.

The local ghost hunters will tell you that a faceless monk is sometimes seen walking around Paradise. But then, they believe stories about floating orbs and missing dogs in Clapham Woods. They also like fizzy lager with cheese and onion crisps. So we can safely ignore what *they* have to say. Even on those evenings when – despite all the street lamps and car headlights – it seems unusually dark around Paradise.

Like tonight.

IV

THE CORN EXCHANGE

Carol Thomas

Having seen everybody off the premises Jess Simmonds drank the last drop of wine from her glass. She knew it wasn't exactly champagne and Next in Chichester was hardly Harrods but nevertheless becoming manager of such a big shop at the age of twenty-five was an achievement.

Switching the lights off on the first floor Jess looked out into the street below. She could see a small group of people gathered outside on the pavement, wrapped in warm coats and scarves against the chill evening air. It was almost Halloween and by the look of it they were on one of the many ghost walks happening across the city.

The woman leading the group was reading aloud with everyone else gathered around her; her breath rose into the air like ethereal plumes of smoke with every word adding to the drama in her expression. Jess couldn't resist making a "whoooooo" noise and laughed at her own joke.

Doing her last checks across the store, gathering her things and turning off the ground floor lights, she realised she had exactly ten minutes to get to The Nag's Head to meet her boyfriend. Steve wasn't the kind of person to be kept waiting, even if you did have celebrating your promotion as an excuse.

As she opened the door Jess was met by a blast of cold air. The group remained outside, the storyteller's voice becoming increasingly animated as she continued to tell her tale. Jess rolled her eyes and hurriedly tried to lock the door until the woman's words caused her to freeze.

"The first recorded sighting of the ghost of Jessica Simmonds, here at the Corn Exchange was in 1952, when it was a cinema. A child reported seeing a young woman staring back at her from the large mirror in the entrance of the auditorium. Several sightings have been made since. It is thought that Jessica always appears as a reflection, over the years being seen in mirrors and in the glass shop frontage. Watching, waiting for something, we don't know what.

"Investigations into the history of the building show that Jessica Simmonds, aged twenty-five, was murdered here on this very site in 1948. It is thought she was killed by her jealous boyfriend, who beat her and hid her body in a nearby alleyway, where it lay undiscovered until Halloween night."

With that the group moved on, muttering about the gruesome revelations. Jess looked up, jumping at her own reflection in the glass door. Cursing the fact she had let the stupid name coincidence scare her, Jess let out a steadying breath. But as she did so she couldn't help but notice the plume of smoke from her own mouth was not reflected in the window. It wasn't there as she breathed harder, her pulse racing, it wasn't there as she saw Steve appear behind her.

And it wasn't there as her reflection whispered, "You've found me."

V

ODE TO A GHOST WALK

Jenny Dean

'And it's a very reasonable rent, sir,' mentioned Mr Black casually as Darren followed him up the dark, narrow staircase. 'Especially for accommodation in the centre of Chichester.'

The student nodded. It suited his meagre finances as a literature student at the university as much as its situation did. As he looked around the small, low-ceilinged room, he tasted its sweet, damp odour and smelt the darkness of its walls. He shivered as an icy wind flew through the open casement window and pushed him against the old wooden desk in the corner. Darren smoothed his hand along its rugged surface and felt the crude marks inlaid there. He turned and read 'My darling love, F.B.' 'Hmm, interesting,' he thought. The initials nagged at him, an allusion he couldn't quite reach.

'Of course, gas and electricity are extra but as the property has been vacant for some time, we're prepared to offer a discount on the heating. After all,' the landlord laughed, 'we are in the middle of winter.'

Darren was desperate. His course was due to start in two days' time, the 21st, and he needed somewhere to study, so ignoring his body's red light, he butted in. 'I'll take it. Now.'

'I'm sure you'll be delighted with it, sir.' A pause then, 'A very special person has inhabited it, you know.'

'Oh?' Darren was curious. 'Who?'

'Oh, that'd be telling. And for you to find out. Let's just say this time of year was significant to him.' And, with papers signed and deposit handed over in minutes, Mr Black was gone and the student was left alone with only a rickety bed, a tatty chair and the old wooden desk for company.

Ducking his head out of the small window he breathed in the view below the barber's. The icy road was a caterpillar of vehicles. Darren closed the window promptly on the easterly wind and, wrapping his anorak tightly around him, stamped his feet violently to get warm. Slow creaks from the dried wood followed him around the room like a stalker on an empty lane. 'I'll get used to it,' Darren comforted himself. 'I'll feel better when I've had some sleep.'

Little daylight was left as Darren dropped his few belongings around the edges of the room and switched on the light. The gloom remained, a thick paste as shadows crept across the walls and wrapped their fingers around him. 'Time to go out,' he thought and, snatching up his coat, Darren stumbled down the thin stairs and into the enticing January night.

But Darren hadn't been in the mood. Not for his mates. Not for a beer and, despite the warmth of the snug bar at the Agnes Arms, he had felt chilled to the bone and couldn't shake off the flat's wintry hand. And the landlord's puzzle nagged at him. Darren knew the answer, he was sure he did.

'How about we come back to yours?' Alan had moved. 'Celebrate your new pad.'

'Not just now,' Darren had said. 'I need a kip.' And he'd left with barely a few words spoken all evening.

Although Darren was stark sober as he let himself in, he felt filled with a dread as deep as drink. Why the sense of something untoward about his room? It was dingy, damp and cold like many old buildings but he felt something else. He just didn't know what.

He gingerly removed his coat and slowly slipped between the mattress and blanket. He would make up the bed tomorrow, he thought, and closed his eyes. 'Sleep, sleep. Please come', he prayed and waited. And waited.

It was when the cathedral clock struck two that he heard it. At first, the muffled crying of a young man then the rising sobs and howls of despair. He turned, in the darkness, to the source of distress, lying beside him in the bed. There was no-one there! His body petrified like molten rock whilst his heart knocked on his ribcage for freedom. 'Help me! Help me someone!'

He was unsure whether it was he who had spoken or the ghostly voice in the bed. Not until a crackling cough tore through the air then erupted over the room did he finally believe it wasn't he. But still Darren couldn't sleep for the coughing continued relentlessly, intermingled with the tears of the invisible form.

Eventually the young man fell into some sort of slumber, so exhausted was he in body and mind. But rest seemed to be his enemy that night for, soon, he was deep in the arms of a riveting dream of which he was the hero. He'd entered the room by the casement window and found his love lying on the bed. She'd waited so long for him but knew that he would come to her. For hadn't she performed the rituals necessary, on this auspicious night, for her dream to come true? 'I shall take you away', he'd cried. 'We shall escape our families' hostility to our love.'

And then he was awake. Awake to the screams of the buses stopping outside in the cold daylight. He turned to look at his watch and saw, instead, the deep red blood hardened into a scab on the pillow beside him. Alert, he jumped up and rushed to the window. There, beside the desk, beneath it, lay crumpled balls of paper. Picking one up, he read...

> *'She seemed a splendid angel, newly drest*
> *Save wings for heaven– I grew faint..'*

Darren recognised the lines and gave a little laugh – John Keats' famous poem written for this day! And FB now revealed their origins to him – was not FB Fanny Brawne, the love of Keats, although he had died too soon to marry her? A bemused Darren thrust his head out of the window for air, only to be met by a melee of shrill voices beneath him. Suddenly a path was cleared amongst the throng and a covered stretcher, carried by two heavy figures, emerged from the barber's.

Hurtling down the stairs as fast as his staggering legs would allow and into the barber's shop, Darren suddenly stopped. He knew instinctively what had happened. Mr Black, the landlord, was dead. And he knew why. He checked his watch. Yes. The date was correct.

And he knew, then, who owned the sobbing voice and the reason for his dream.

NOTES:

Keats began to write his poem 'The Eve of St Agnes' at 11 Eastgate Square. St Agnes Eve takes place on 21st January.

The 'F.B.' carved in the desk are the initials of Keats' girlfriend, Fanny Brawne.

VI

REACHING OUT

Helen Christmas

Nature called. Had I imagined it, or was it dark when I tiptoed downstairs? Not quite...

It must have been dawn, the first grey light pushing its way through a gap in the sitting room curtains. I paused and saw the emerging beam as it fell across the room, parting the shadows, teasing away the gloom. It was a yawning, slightly hazy yellow light, stirring the dust motes.

I was only stood still for a second when something in the room shifted; a shape blending into the beam. But it was not a shadow – more an outline, the dust motes clinging to the edge of something invisible, a silhouette ... I froze as a movement passed across the lounge. It was without substance but nevertheless left the impression of an old lady, bent over a stick, shuffling slowly past. The vision was so subliminal, it was forgotten almost instantly.

Somewhere in the blur of my mind it had registered but the clouds of sleepiness were pressing down heavily, suppressing it, as I slithered back upstairs, back to the sanctuary of my warm bed.

A little later while clearing out some drawers I found an old guest book with the first entry written in May 1914, "A lovely week with the Christmases."

I asked my husband, Peter, if his Great Aunt Marie had lived here all her life, as she passed on just before we met in 1996. He believed she had moved in with her parents and brother to help their Gran run it as a B&B during the Great War. They were still doing it by the time WWII arrived. He handed me a diary, a small handwritten journal in which Marie had chronicled what she remembered about her own family before her 100th birthday.

"I've tried to search through the deeds, being all in old English & faint with age, my sight not as good these days, cannot see very well, so this may not be quite correct as to dates. The first date I can find is 1756, in a will of an ancestor, Mr John Quinnoll, whose daughter Grace married John Yeates.

John Yeates' daughter, Fanny, married Mr Boorn. I'm not sure if her name was Fanny or Mary, as she was always Gran to me. A little bent old lady, who walked with a stick, but sweetness personified, crippled through a fall downstairs, which was never treated..."

I stopped reading. Fingers of cold brushed my shoulders, sweeping over my entire body like a shroud as it was only then the memory drifted back to me. I am sure our lovely home was trying to tell me something. The presence has never really left me.

NOTES:

Yet again we have to confess that this ghost story, whilst true, happened at a cottage in Bognor Regis, not Chichester.

VII

LITTLE BILLY

Caroline Travis

Billy and Lizzie were the only children of William Morrey, master butcher to the city of Chichester, and his wife, Annie. William idolised his young and beautiful wife and thanked his great and merciful God every day for his excellent good fortune.

When Annie fell with their youngest child, she experienced many discomforts. As she carried and nurtured the growing life she somehow knew that this time the baby would be a boy, to be named after his father. But as the child started to thrive so Annie started to dive, coughing a little more each day. Thus little Billy was only four years old when consumption finally carried his mother off to meet her maker. The devastated and inconsolable William took his desolation to the nearest alehouse.

The Old Cross Inn was also frequented by the sour-faced Master of the Chichester workhouse, James Dewey, who had long held grudges against the butcher. Dewey, a grasping, greedy miser, angry that the world thought his work worth a mere £25 a year, revelled in the butcher's misery and misfortune and, under the auspices of cheering the widower up, cheated him of his business and his home. And so, on the 29th October 1859 little Billy and his six-year-old sister were marched to the workhouse in New Broyle Road.

Billy was put to work in the crushing yard. His job was to fill the sacks, woven and sewn by desperate women, with bone pulverised by the beleaguered old men, to be sold as fertiliser. Lizzie was set to work washing and chopping vegetables and washing pots and dishes.

That first night, Lizzie tumbled into her pit and immediately fell into an exhausted sleep. But as little Billy closed his eyes, the Assistant Master, Dewey's equally repulsive and despotic son, Jonas, taking immense pleasure in frightening Morrey's helpless child, took little Billy next door to the Dead

Room. The room was in the far north-east corner with a barred, unglazed window in each of the outside walls. As the unusually cold wind whistled through, Jonas lifted the little waif and laid him on top of the corpse of a toothless, open-mouthed old woman and warned him that any trouble from the little guttersnipe and this would be where he slept.

As Billy huddled in his cot afterwards, the wind blowing through from the Dead Room next door seemed to be whispering to him. Every time he closed his eyes he could see the old woman next door, rising from her coffin and moving towards him, her arms outstretched. Eventually poor Billy slipped into a deep and troubled sleep.

The next morning when the bell clanged everyone awake at half past five, the Assistant Master found that Billy's 'mattress' (for want of a better word) was sodden with the child's urine. His punishment was to be *'sett upon a stool during dinner with a paper fixed to his breast whereon shall be wrote in capital letters BED WETTER'*. Lizzie's eyes pricked with tears when she saw his shame and the dark blue circles around his eyes.

The second night, Lizzie stayed awake hoping that she would be able to sneak in and comfort the shrinking form of her little brother. But as soon as she put her feet on the floor, the mistress's assistant set upon her and tied Lizzie to the bed. Later that night little Billy, exhausted and terrified, again lost control.

The third night, little Billy held his head high as the Assistant Master again placed the *BED WETTER* sign over his head. This annoyed the tyrant so much that Billy was sentenced to sleep that night in the very place that had made him wet his bed.

Lizzie never saw her little brother again, but, over a meatier than average broth later that week, the mistress told her that he'd been apprenticed to Mr Crip the chimney sweep.

Even now, if a freezing north easterly blows on Halloween, the smell of meat broth accompanied by the sound of Lizzie, screaming her brother's name, can be heard in New Broyle Road.

VIII

THE CRYING CATACOMBS OF CHICHESTER

Becky Brooke

The crumbling tunnel swelled with blackness until the very air was thick with a greedy dark void that filled every nook and cranny. Charlie's skin felt slick with sweat and deathly cold. He couldn't see his hands in front of his face but he held them outstretched for protection against the rough tunnel walls.

How long had he been walking? The question fluttered around the periphery of his mind ... he just couldn't remember.

He lifted a thick-fingered hand to the back of his neck swiping at the irritating stickiness there. His worn hobnail boots crunched along the tunnel floor, each step sounding like an explosion piercing the complete silence.

His eyes, large and dark, flitted left to right desperate to find the steps that led up to the way out. *Nancy would be waiting with dinner, wondering where he was. How long had he been gone?* He remembered the summons for all the commoners to come to the Guild Hall earlier that day for the election ... *was it the same day?* He had been nervous. He knew the dark, dangerous secret kept by Mr Johnson who stood for election and he was sure Mr Johnson knew that he knew.

He remembered dashing in for a drink of Dutch courage at the George and Dragon beforehand, and then bumping into Billy and the boys after leaving. They'd then walked the short distance to the meeting together. Charlie, sweating and shaky when they arrived, sneaked off round the side of the building for a quick smoke before it all started. Just to gather his thoughts and nerves and figure out what he was going to do about that strange disturbing secret.

His hands had been unsteady and he could barely light his pipe. The wind had whipped up and extinguished the light that he had finally managed to strike up. Cursing, he had turned to find a better shelter...then an intense feeling of heat and pain had shot though the back of his head, and hot blood trickled down the back of his neck. He heard a noise behind him and saw Billy. But it did not look like the Billy he knew … this Billy wore a twisted smile and his eyes were full of an inky malice that bore down on him as he tilted over. He remembered hearing him start to say something to him in a dark cracked voice …but then the world fell away.

The sound of his boots scraping, being dragged along the gritty street, back towards the public house. *He had just come from there, why was he going back?* Shuddering shocks down his body jolted him awake again as he saw the light fading from above. Downwards, cold stone steps descended away from the light. Several pairs of hands now pulling him into a long tunnel that led towards the vaults. Now the darkness again. His thoughts had surfaced from the last blurry moments of his life. Tears squeezed from his crumpled face as he now realised his Nancy would be waiting all night and he would never come home.

A thundering bellowed from above and shook his very soul – it was the cathedral bells. He howled as he knew his body was lying on the vault floor …but he would walk and weep for his lost love, forever, in the catacombs of Chichester.

IX

MARY JANE'S FATE

Alison Jones

Jones the Bootmakers has a violent past which resonates within its very walls. In 1832 it was a thriving public house. Many a merchant would frequent it for a tankard of ale after plying their wares at the Market Cross. The company was convivial and the publican and his wife considered to be a jovial and accommodating couple. Mary Jane, the bartender's wife, was an extrovert, buxom wench who could make any man frequenting the tavern feel that she had eyes only for him. This, as she told her husband on numerous occasions, was ridiculous as she was merely plying them with more ale to bolster their profits, and he had no cause to feel jealous. However the doubts regarding her fidelity persistently chipped away inside of him. As she went about her normal business of 'entertaining' each evening he would feel jealous and anxious until what started as an ember of suspicion became a burning fire of doubt and loathing for Mary Jane. So one night in 1834 after a packed evening of drinking and hilarity, the publican pushed his last customer a little the worse for wear out of the front door and wearily drew the bolt across. Mary Jayne had already retired, claiming that she had 'one of her heads'. Well, he wasn't surprised, the amount that she had drunk. It was a disgrace the way she acted and she should be ashamed of herself. He had no other plan than to slip into the bed next to her, turn his back and go to sleep; however, in the flickering gas light he thought he could see a smile cross her face and the murmur of one of his regulars' names pass her lips. He knew not what came over him, it seemed as though he was beset by a jealous rage that filled his whole body, bursting to get out and sate itself on poor Mary Jane in her slumber. He put his hands around her throat, every sinew in his body tensed, intent on the task in hand, to wipe the smile off his wife's face and teach her that a woman must stay faithful to her man and not gallivant about, drinking ale and cavorting with all and sundry. It was a good five

47

minutes before he let go of her neck; she had long since died, and he hadn't even noticed. He tucked the bedclothes around her and then calmly handed himself in at the local peelers' station. Within three months he was hung on the gibbet outside Chichester for his crime. The pub closed and much later became this boot shop, although I have heard tell that sometimes you may get more than a pair of boots here: if you are particularly unlucky you may feel a pair of hands grasping tight at your neck.

Printed in Great Britain
by Amazon

41452002R00030